# Color your worries away!

*Be more relaxed, focused, and energized! Coloring helps you exp**ity.*
*Find your own style in the pages that follow. Here are some ideas to get you started.*

## Color Theory 101

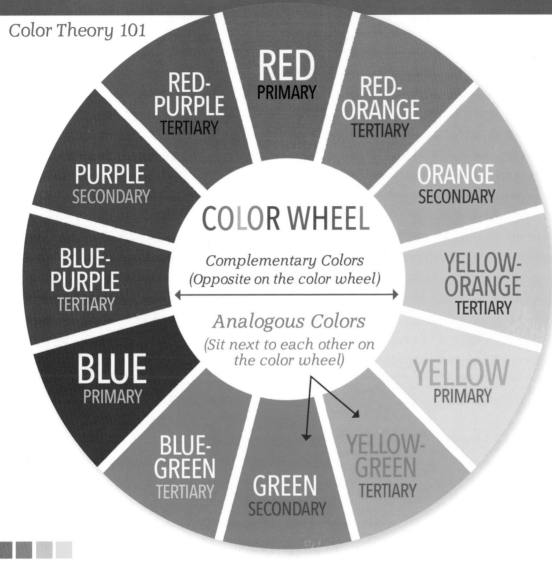

**COLOR WHEEL**

*Complementary Colors*
*(Opposite on the color wheel)*

*Analogous Colors*
*(Sit next to each other on the color wheel)*

- RED — PRIMARY
- RED-PURPLE — TERTIARY
- PURPLE — SECONDARY
- BLUE-PURPLE — TERTIARY
- BLUE — PRIMARY
- BLUE-GREEN — TERTIARY
- GREEN — SECONDARY
- YELLOW-GREEN — TERTIARY
- YELLOW — PRIMARY
- YELLOW-ORANGE — TERTIARY
- ORANGE — SECONDARY
- RED-ORANGE — TERTIARY

### Warm Colors
Warm colors are vivid and energetic.

### Cool Colors
Cool colors are calm and soothing.

### Complementary Colors
Use complementary color when you want to emphasize the colors. They naturally play off one another and make each other look more vivid and intense.

### Analogous Colors
Use analogous colors when you want more than one color but want to maintain a sense of unity.

### Primary Colors
Primary colors can't be mixed or made. Different combinations of primary colors create all other traditional colors.

### Secondary Colors
Combining two primary colors together creates a secondary color.

### Tertiary Colors
Combining a primary and a secondary color results in a tertiary color. You may know them by their fancier names like "teal" or "lime green" but they are referred to by the two colors that make them up, with the primary color first.

*art* UNPLUGGED

A NATURAL
SOURCE OF
HEALING

*Stippling is filling in space with tiny dots–tightly packed, spread out, or however you want to place them. This can add texture and interest to your designs.*

*Hatching is filling space with a series of separate parallel lines.*

*Cross-hatching is drawing a layer of hatching and then adding a second layer of hatching in another direction, on top. It can give the illusion of depth and shading.*

*Back-and-forth stroke ("scribbling") is a simple continuous motion to fill in space with a solid color. Do it without lifting your pencil or marker off the page.*

*Circular stroke is another way to fill a space with solid color: moving your pencil or marker continuously in overlapping circles.*

## Tip: Keep Your Colors Safe

*Store your colored pencils somewhere safe, where they won't be dropped or shuffled around. That will protect the lead inside your pencils and keep it from cracking, so your pencils sharpen cleanly and easily.*

# Adding Texture and Layers and Detail

*Sharp colored pencils and fine markers are great for coloring delicate details.*

*You can add textures and depth by starting with a light color and then going back and coloring over it with a darker color, or pressing down harder with the same pencil or marker.*

*Different colors can be blended together in a smooth transition.*

Use a cotton swab lightly dipped in baby oil to soften hard edges or smooth two blending colors together.

Add white highlights with a gel pen, or a fine brush with white paint, to look like light reflecting on a surface.

# Water Wonders

art
UNPLUGGED

A NATURAL
SOURCE OF
HEALING

*This EXPERIENCE belongs to:*

©2016 Art-Unplugged
4001 Helton Drive • P.O. Box 782 • Florence, Alabama 35631

For helpful tips, examples, and inspiration, please visit: **art-unplugged.me**

Illustration by Marlene Minker
Design by Tanya Wagner

This book is not intended as a substitute for the advice of a mental-health-care provider. The publisher encourages taking personal responsibility for your own mental, physical, and spiritual well-being.

Quotes included in this book have been researched with due diligence and our best intentions, and we believe them to be historically accurate. Please send any queries or corrections to the address above.

**Look for the entire series of art-unplugged journals.**

ISBN: 1940899184 (Water Wonders)

Printed in the United States of America

*"Sweat is the cologne of accomplishment."*

*– Heywood Hale Broun*

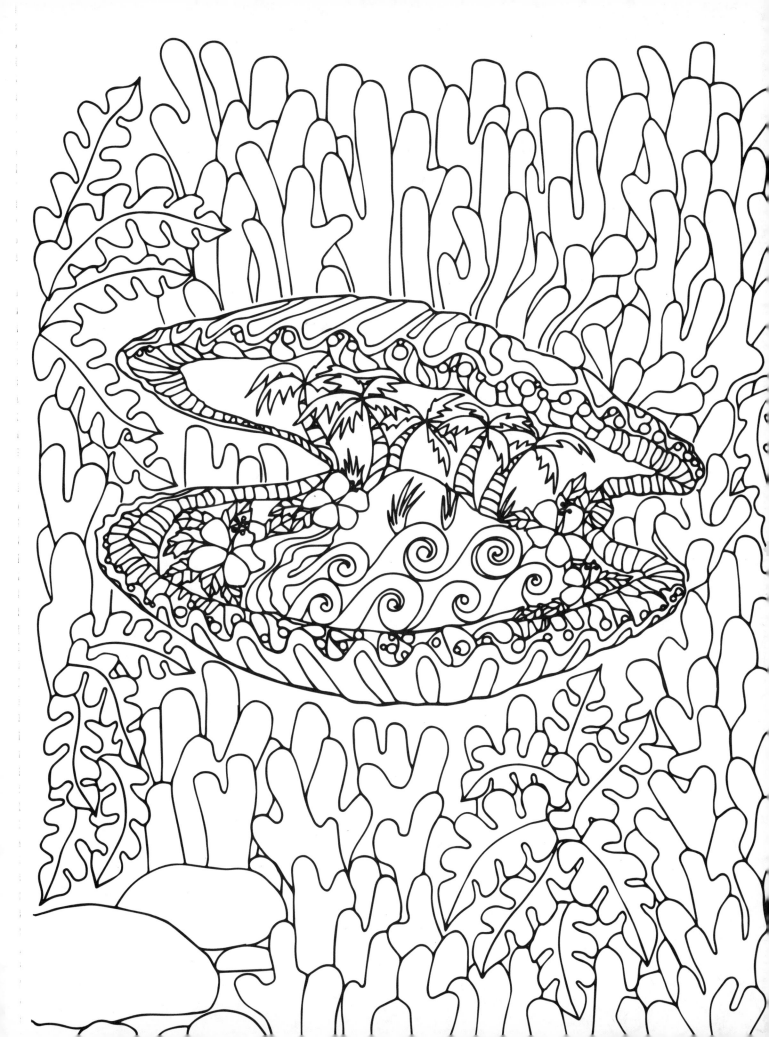

*What are ways that you express joy?*
*What colors represent joy for you?*

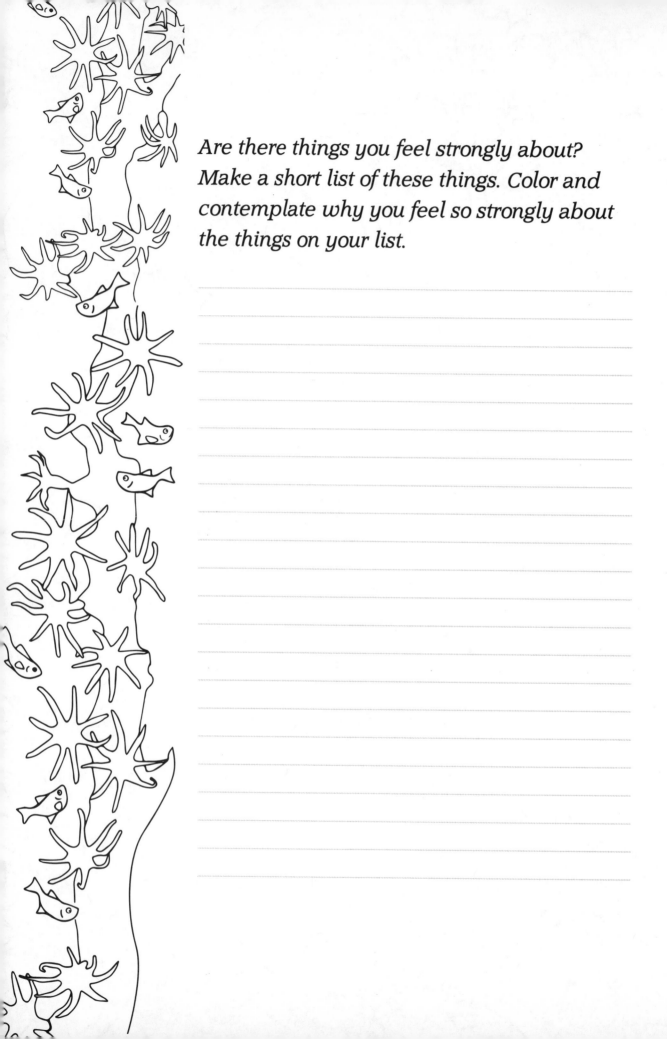

Are there things you feel strongly about?
Make a short list of these things. Color and
contemplate why you feel so strongly about
the things on your list.

*"A journey of a thousand miles
begins with a single step."*

*– Proverb*

*"Your calling is the place where your deep gladness and the world's deep hunger meet."*

*– Frederick Buechner*

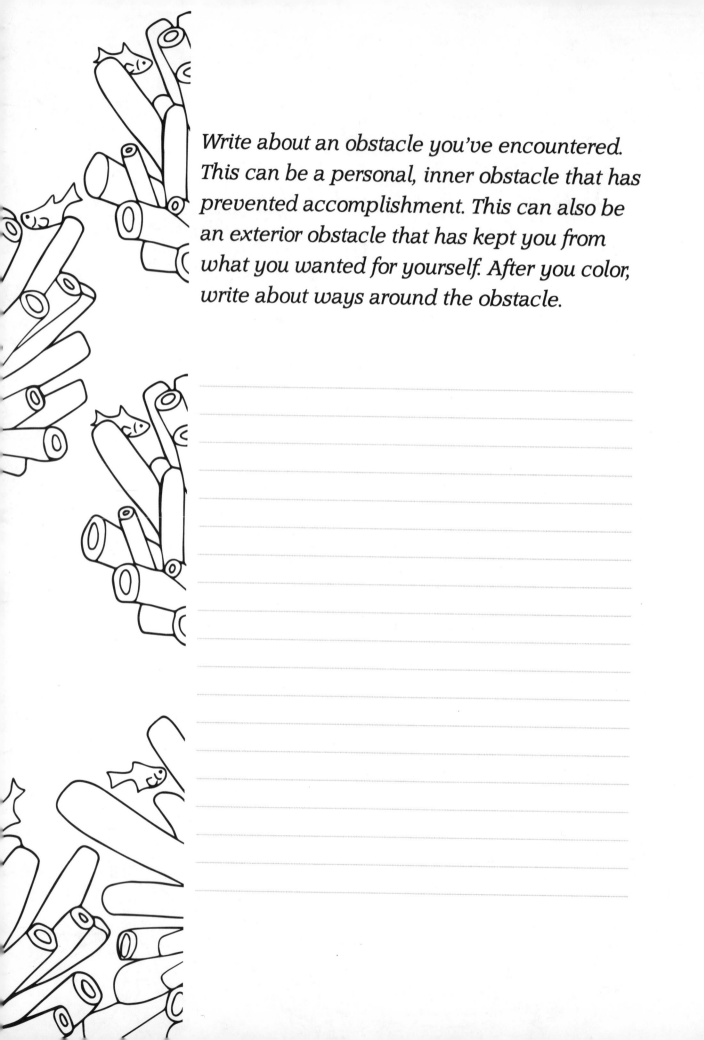

Write about an obstacle you've encountered. This can be a personal, inner obstacle that has prevented accomplishment. This can also be an exterior obstacle that has kept you from what you wanted for yourself. After you color, write about ways around the obstacle.

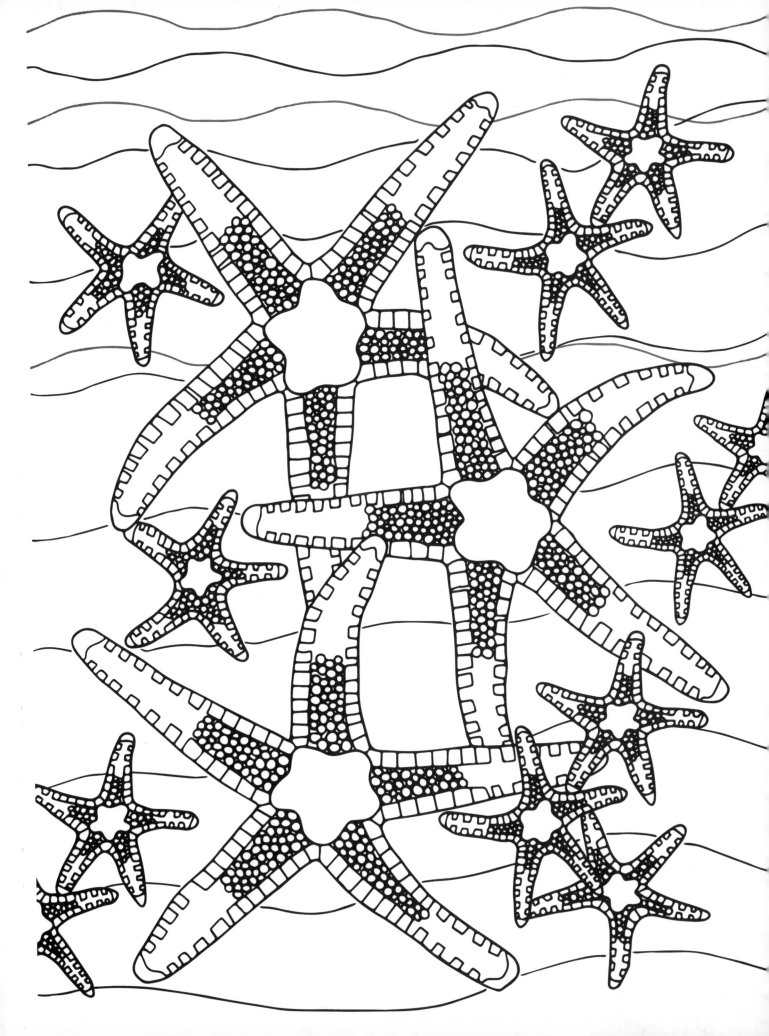

*"Strong convictions are the secret of surviving deprivation; your spirit can be full even when your stomach is empty."*

– Nelson Mandela

As you color, think of something you have always wanted to do but never done. Write about why you have never done this thing. Then write about how you can change this for yourself.

*"There are short-cuts to happiness, and dancing is one of them."*

*– Vicki Baum*

*Sometimes colors trigger memories. What memories do the colors you've chosen for this page trigger?*

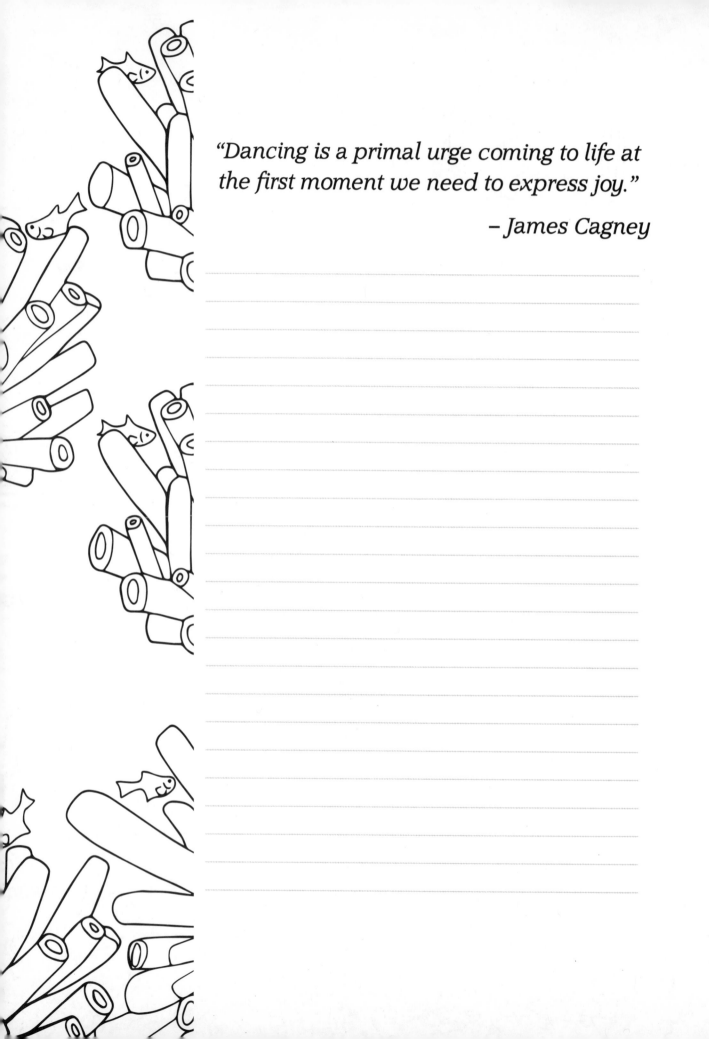

*"Dancing is a primal urge coming to life at the first moment we need to express joy."*

– James Cagney

"A discovery is said to be an accident meeting a prepared mind."

– Unknown

Is there an activity that brings you joy? Is it an activity involving others or is does it just involve you? Is it an activity that is a habit? If yes, why? If no, what keeps you from doing it often?

*"The trouble with having an open mind,
of course, is that people will insist on
coming along and trying to put things in it."*

*– Terry Pratchett*

*What have you discovered about yourself as you color? Think of at least three things that coloring has taught you about yourself and write those things down.*

"The reason I talk to myself is because I'm the only one whose answers I accept."

– George Carlin

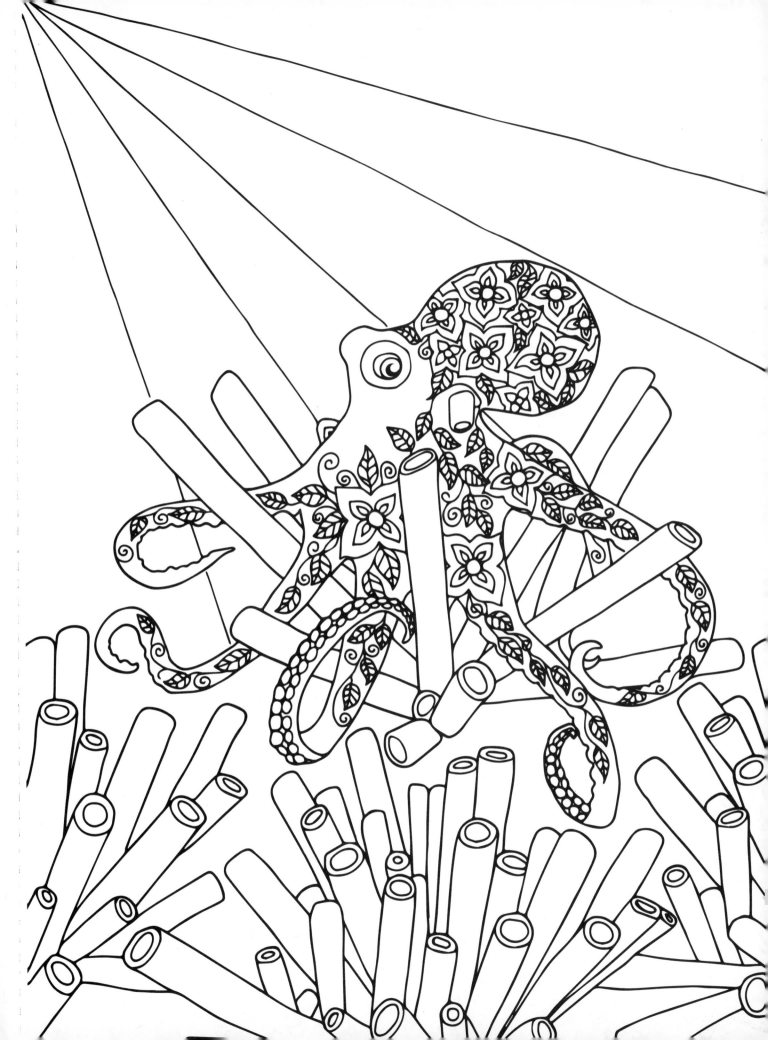

*In what ways does coloring open your mind to new ideas? Consider this and write about how this activity opens you to new ideas.*

*"We often discover what will do, by finding out what will not do; and probably he who never made a mistake never made a discovery."*

– Samuel Smiles

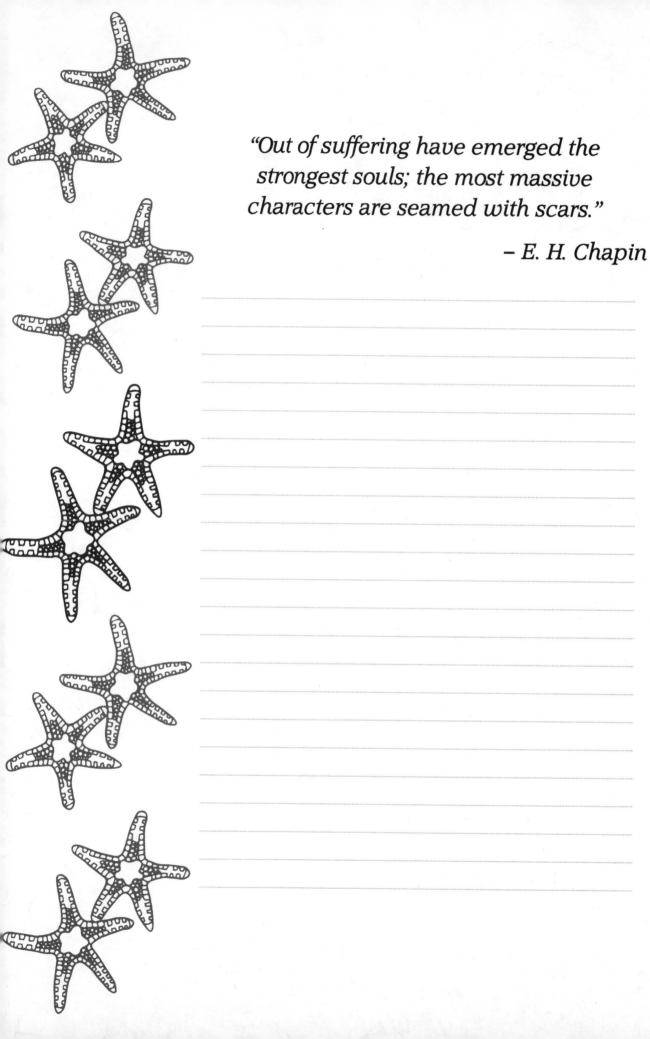

*"Out of suffering have emerged the strongest souls; the most massive characters are seamed with scars."*

*– E. H. Chapin*

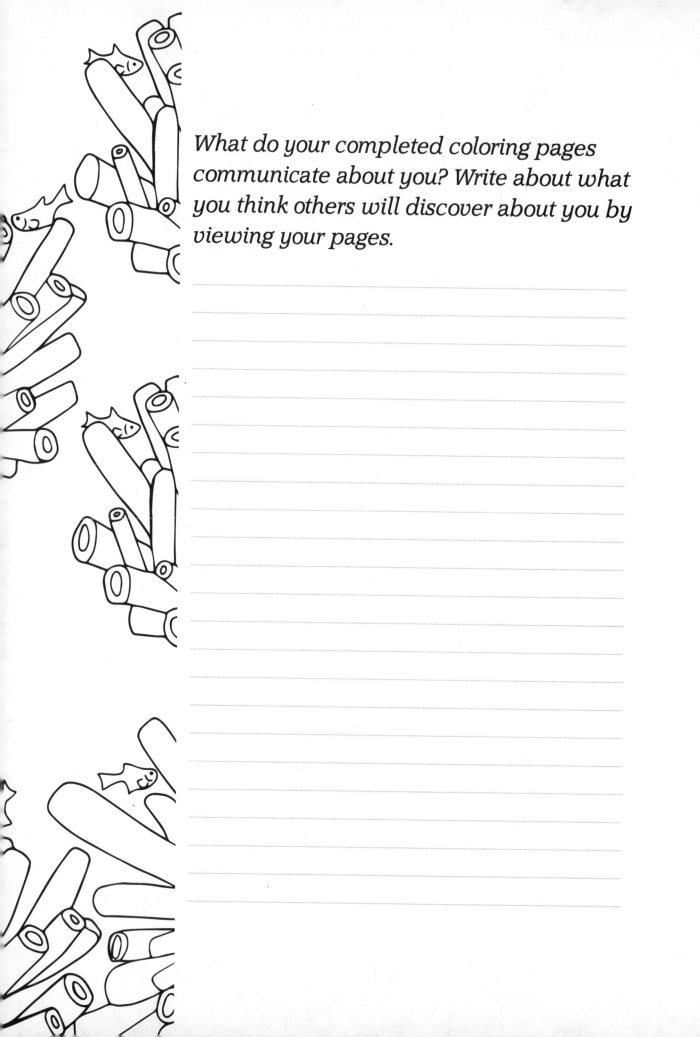

*What do your completed coloring pages communicate about you? Write about what you think others will discover about you by viewing your pages.*

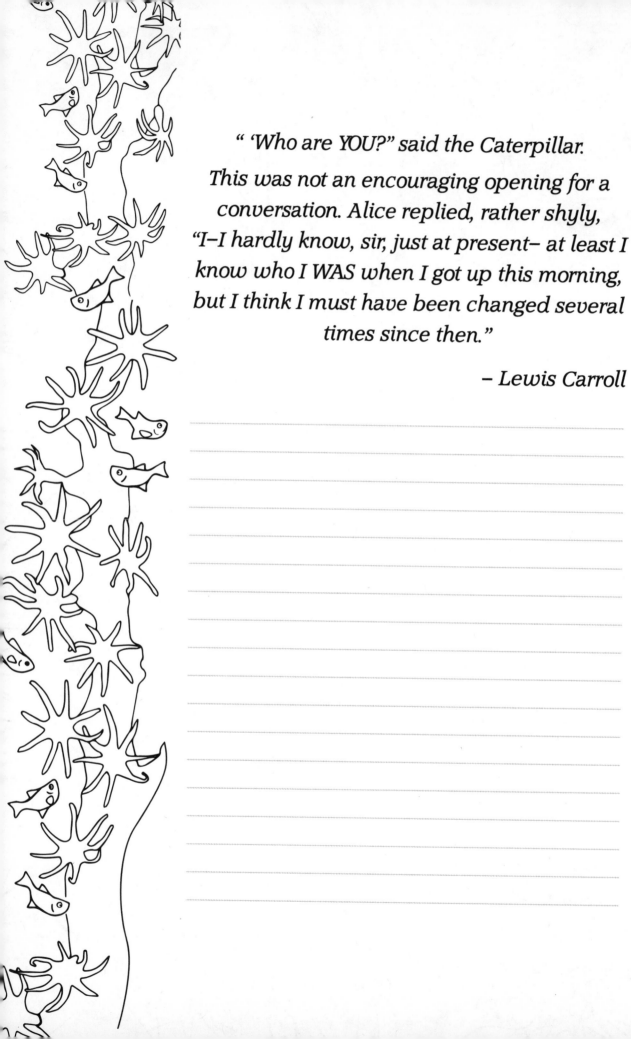

" 'Who are YOU?" said the Caterpillar.

This was not an encouraging opening for a conversation. Alice replied, rather shyly, "I–I hardly know, sir, just at present– at least I know who I WAS when I got up this morning, but I think I must have been changed several times since then."

– Lewis Carroll

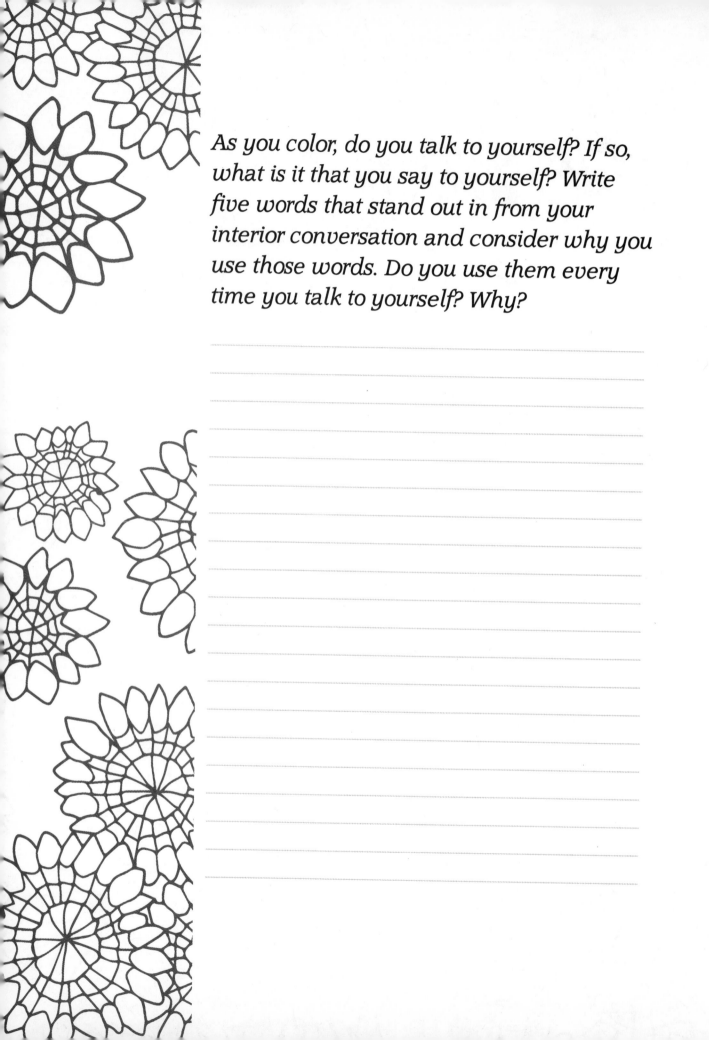

As you color, do you talk to yourself? If so, what is it that you say to yourself? Write five words that stand out in from your interior conversation and consider why you use those words. Do you use them every time you talk to yourself? Why?

*"Every act of conscious learning requires the willingness to suffer an injury to one's self-esteem."*

*– Thomas Szasz*

Consider the things you would never try.
Make a list. Then write the reasons why
you would never try these things. Which
reasons make sense? Which reasons don't
seem to make sense?

*"Trust your hunches. They're usually based
on facts filed away just below
your conscious level."*

*– Joyce Brothers*

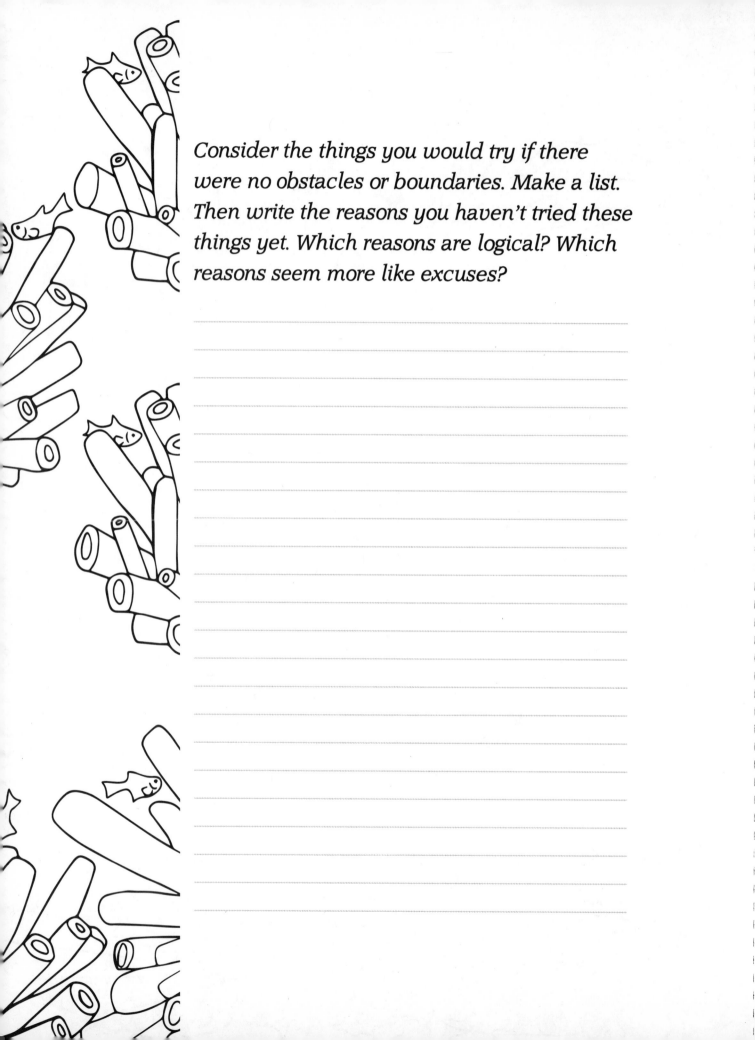

Consider the things you would try if there were no obstacles or boundaries. Make a list. Then write the reasons you haven't tried these things yet. Which reasons are logical? Which reasons seem more like excuses?

*"As one goes through life one learns that if you don't paddle your own canoe, you don't move."*

*– Katharine Hepburn*

*What hard things have you lived through? As you color, think of how these hard things have made you as beautiful as what you are creating on the page. Write a short page about the beauty and color you find in your scars.*

*"Poetry is to be found nowhere
unless we carry it within us."*

– Joseph Joubert

*What is your personal definition of the impossible? Write about this definition. Contemplate the impossible as you color.*

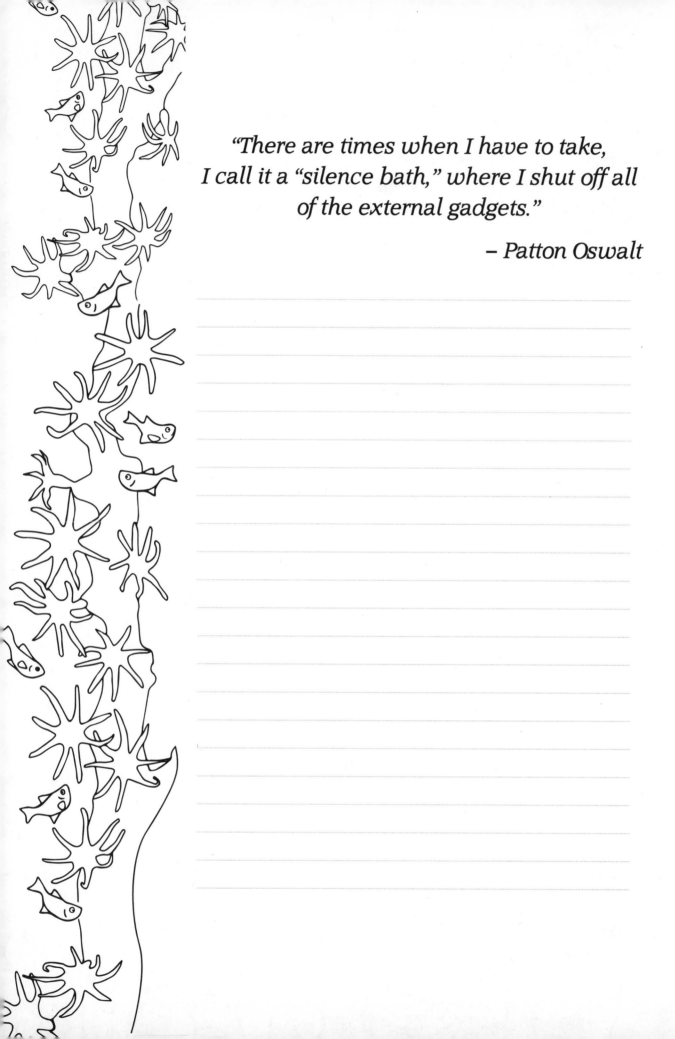

"There are times when I have to take,
I call it a "silence bath," where I shut off all
of the external gadgets."

– Patton Oswalt

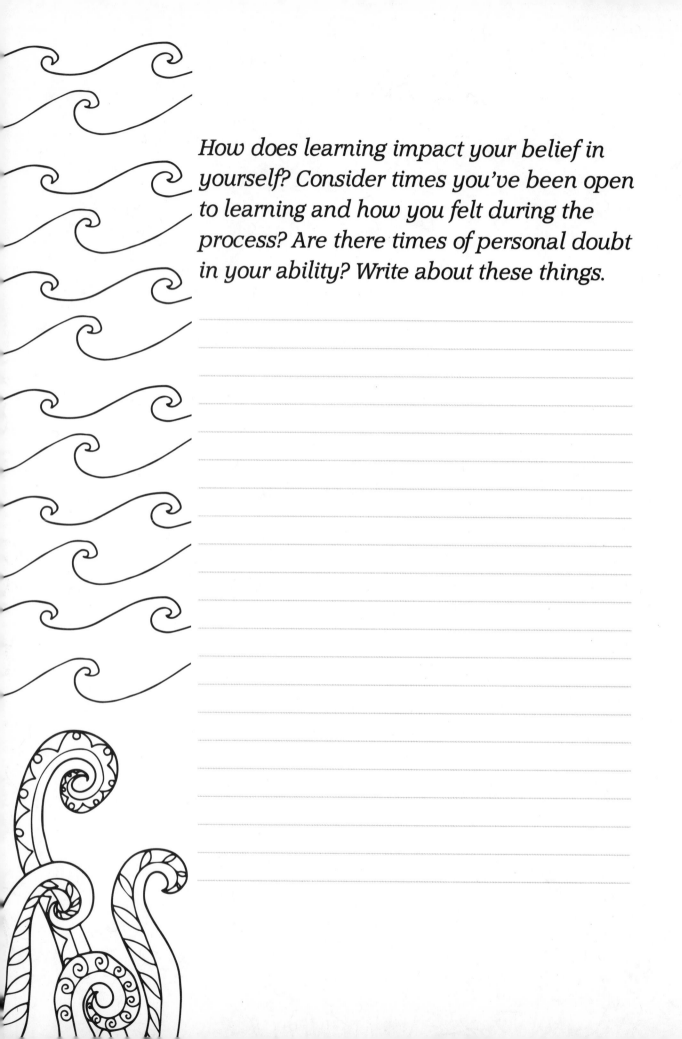

How does learning impact your belief in yourself? Consider times you've been open to learning and how you felt during the process? Are there times of personal doubt in your ability? Write about these things.

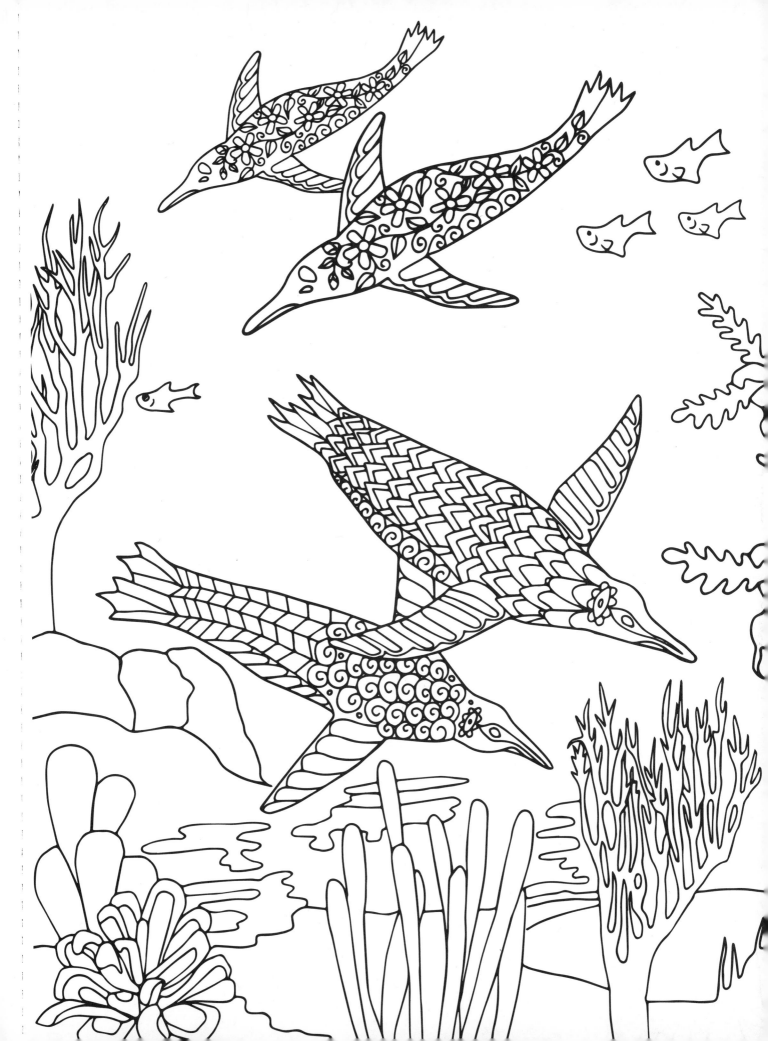

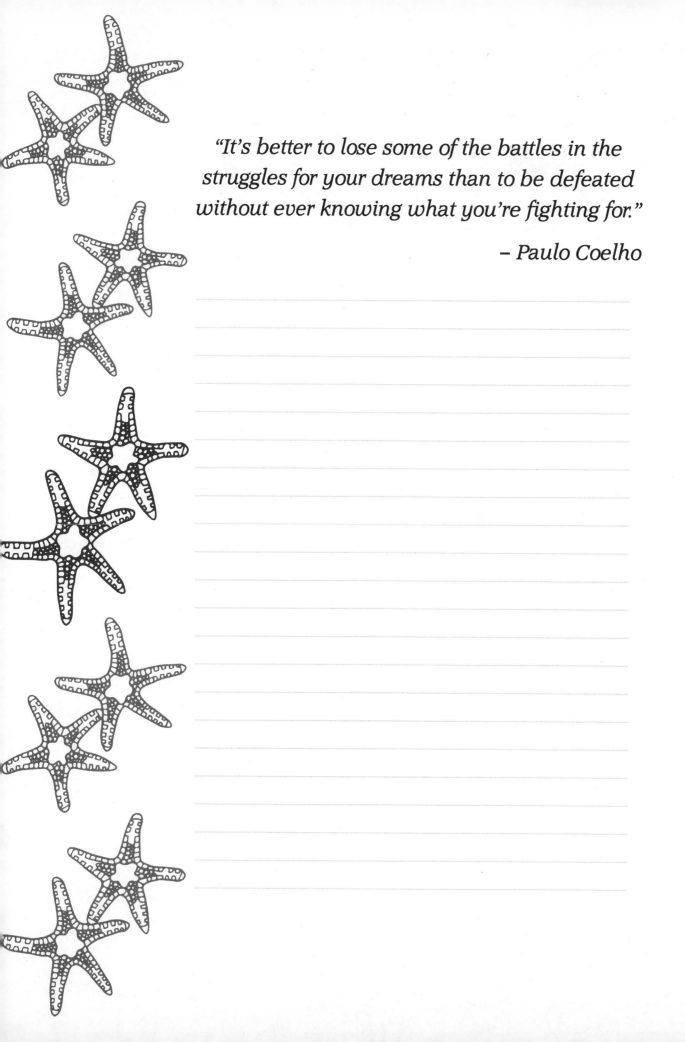

*"It's better to lose some of the battles in the struggles for your dreams than to be defeated without ever knowing what you're fighting for."*

*– Paulo Coelho*

*"Do not feel entitled to anything you do not sweat or struggle for."*

– Marian Wright Edelman

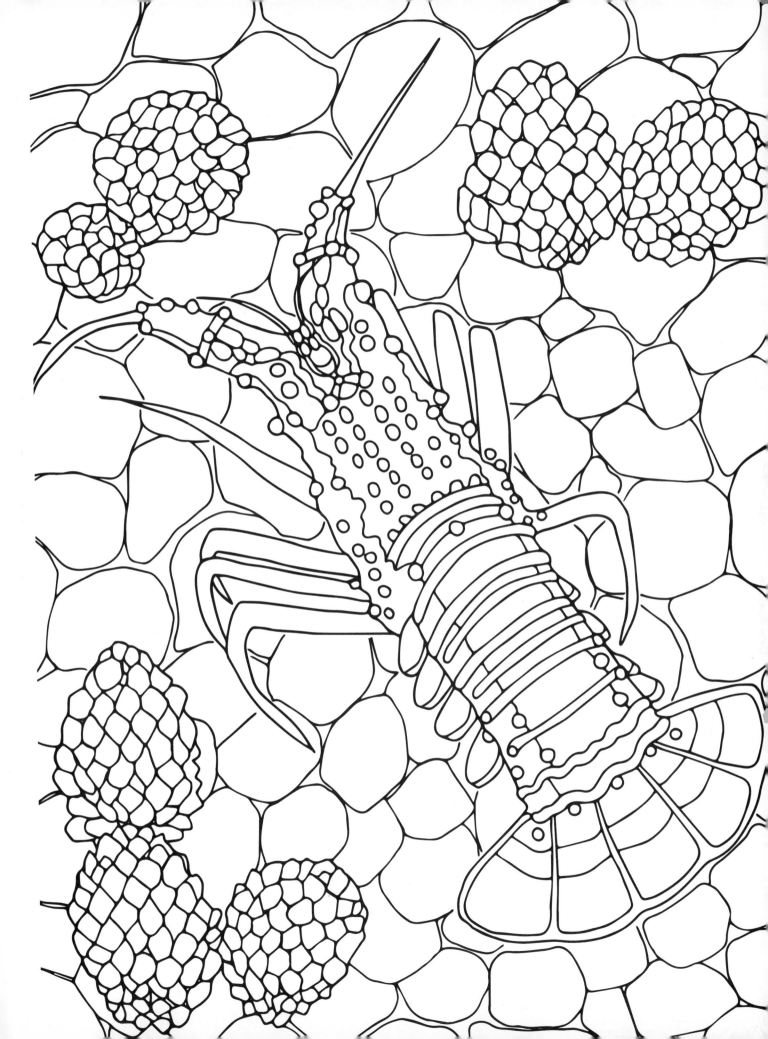

*"Every truth has two sides;*
*it is well to look at both before we*
*commit ourselves to either."*

*– Aesop*

Do you have a dream? As you color, think about this dream. Have you achieved it? If not, what has kept you from this dream? Write about this.

*What is something that you have struggled for? Think of this thing while you color and then write about this struggle.*

Make a list of things that motivate you.
Highlight the ones that are most important to
you. Color and contemplate these motivators.
How can you tap these things to help you
achieve your dreams?

*"Motivation is a fire from within. If someone else tries to light that fire under you, chances are it will burn very briefly."*

– Stephen R. Covey

*"The world breaks everyone and afterward some are strong at the broken places."*

*– Ernest Hemingway*

*Think of one thing you are curious about. Write about that thing and ways that you can learn more about this thing.*

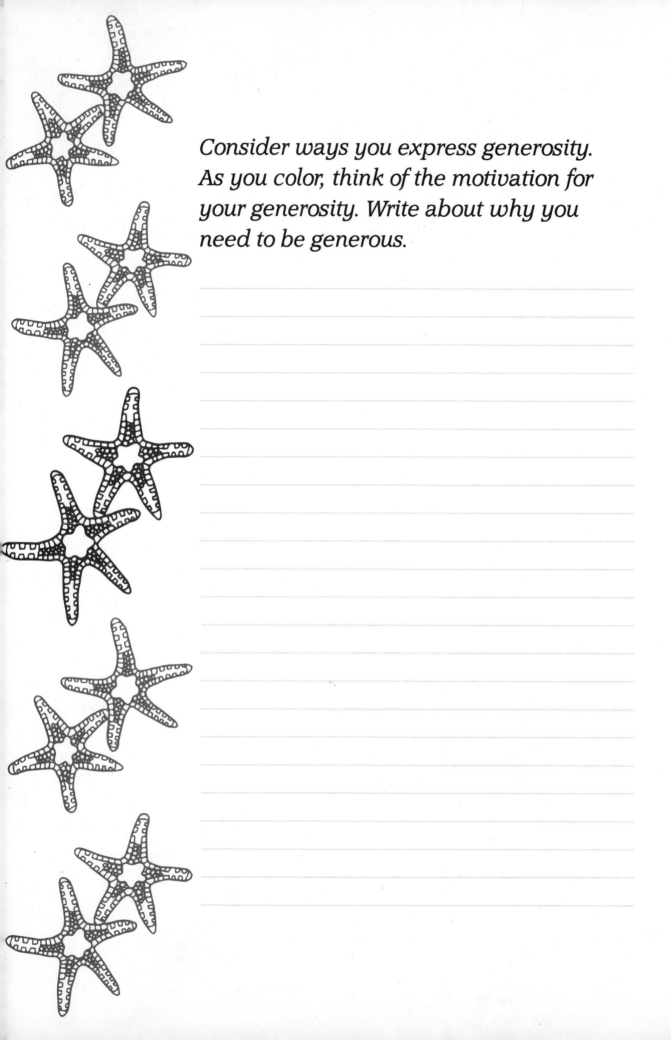

*Consider ways you express generosity.
As you color, think of the motivation for
your generosity. Write about why you
need to be generous.*